Karl Jenkins

The Armed Man:
A Mass For Peace

complete vocal score
SATB and piano

Boosey & Hawkes Music Publishers Ltd
www.boosey.com

Commissioned by the Royal Armouries Museum,
to commemorate the millennium

COMPOSER'S NOTE

The piano reduction in this vocal score is intended for rehearsal purposes only. In performance, either the full orchestral version or the reduced version may be used. The reduced version is scored for optional flute (doubling piccolo), 2 or 3 trumpets, 2 or 3 percussion, organ or synthesizer, and strings; piano and optional solo cello may be used instead of strings. All performance material is available from the publishers.

A choral suite containing selected movements from this work (*Kyrie, Sanctus, Benedictus, Agnus Dei, Hymn Before Action*) is also available (ISMN 979-0-060-11410-6)

Published by Boosey & Hawkes Music Publishers Ltd
Aldwych House
71–91 Aldwych
London
WC2B 4HN

www.boosey.com

© Copyright 2003 by Boosey & Hawkes Music Publishers Ltd

ISMN 979-0-060-11545-5

Reprinted with corrections 2015

Printed by Halstan:
Halstan UK, 2–10 Plantation Road, Amersham, Bucks, HP6 6HJ. United Kingdom
Halstan DE, Weißliliengasse 4, 55116 Mainz. Germany

Images courtesy of Virgin Records Ltd. Karl Jenkins photographed by Mitch Jenkins
Music setting by Andrew Jones

CONTENTS

The Armed Man: A Mass For Peace is available on Virgin CDVE 956 (7243 8 11015 2 0).

The CD features Karl Jenkins conducting The London Philharmonic Orchestra, The National Youth Choir of Great Britain (directed by Michael Brewer) with soloists Tristan Hambleton (treble), Mohammed Gad (muezzin) and BBC Young Musician of the Year 2000, Guy Johnston (cello).

The poignancy and relevance of the work is heightened by the fact that the CD was released on 10 September 2001, the day before the tragic events in the United States.

For further information visit www.karljenkins.com and www.boosey.com

To the victims of Kosovo

THE ARMED MAN

A Mass for Peace

KARL JENKINS

1. The Armed Man

L'Homme armé

Marziale ♩. = 65–70

Tap wood of piano to simulate drum rhythm.

(Piccolo *8va*)

cresc, poco a poco

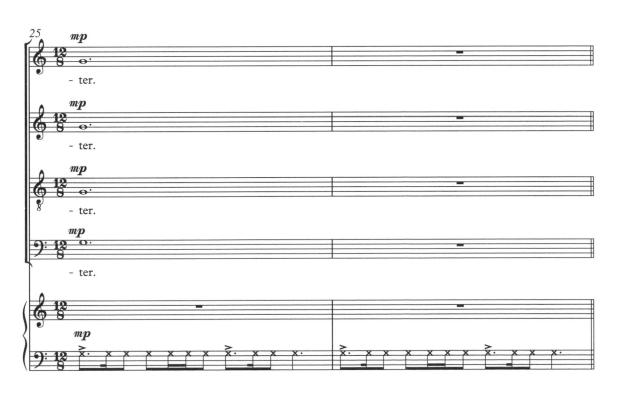

4

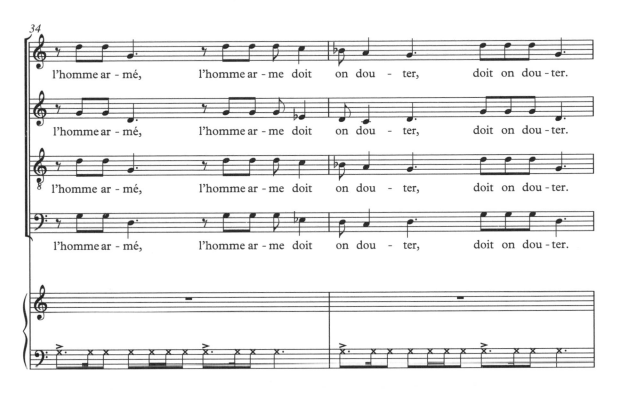

6

6

L'hom - me, l'hom -me, l'homme ar - mé, l'homme ar - mé, l'homme ar - mé doit

L'hom - me, l'hom -me, l'homme ar - mé,

12

14

2. Call to Prayers (Adhaan)

Choir and orchestra tacet

Allahu Akbar
Allahu Akbar

Allahu Akbar
Allahu Akbar

Ashadu An La Illa-L-Lah
Ashadu An La Illa-L-Lah

Ashadu Anna Muhammadan Rasulu-l-lah
Ashadu Anna Muhammadan Rasulu-l-lah

Hayya Ala-s-salah
Hayya Ala-s-salah

Hayya Ala-l-Falah
Hayya Ala-l-Falah

Allahu Akbar
Allahu Akbar

La Illaha il la-lah

3. Kyrie

20

26

4. Save Me from Bloody Men

Psalm 56:1 & 59:2

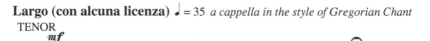

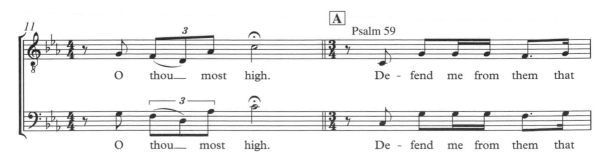

5. Sanctus

34

38

H

6. Hymn Before Action

Text: Rudyard Kipling

The words of Rudyard Kipling are set to music and reproduced by permission of A P Watt Ltd on behalf of
The National Trust for Places of Historical Interest or Natural Beauty.

46

High lust and fro-ward bea - ring, proud heart, re-bell-ious brow,

High lust and fro-ward bea - ring, proud heart, re-bell-ious brow,

High lust and fro-ward bea - ring, proud heart, re-bell-ious brow,

High lust and fro-ward bea - ring, proud heart, re-bell-ious brow,

Deaf ear and soul un - car - - - ing, We seek___ Thy mer-cy now!

The sin-ner that for - swore Thee, The fool___ that passed Thee by,

48

7. Charge!

Text: John Dryden/Jonathan Swift

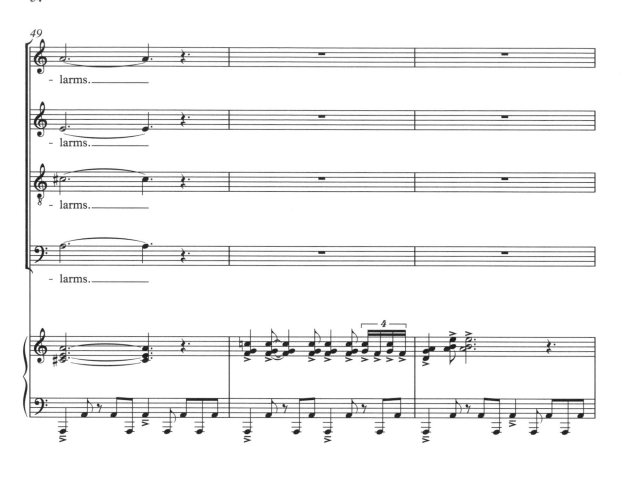

- larms.

- larms.

- larms.

- larms.

The dou-ble double beat of the thun-der-ing drum, the

The dou-ble double beat of the thun-der-ing drum, the

The dou-ble double beat of the thun-der-ing drum, the

The dou-ble double beat of the thun-der-ing drum, the

58

Charge, 'tis too late to re - treat!

Charge, 'tis too late to re - treat!

Charge, 'tis too late to re - treat!

Charge, 'tis too late to re - treat!

F

SOPRANO

How blest is he who for his coun - try dies, who for his coun - try

ALTO

How blest is he who for his coun - try dies, who for his coun - try

The dou-ble dou-ble beat of the
The dou-ble dou-ble beat of the
TENOR The dou-ble dou-ble beat of the
BASS The dou-ble dou-ble beat of the

thun-der-ing drum, the thun-der-ing drum, the thun-der-ing drum. The
thun-der-ing drum, the thun-der-ing drum, the thun-der-ing drum. The
thun-der-ing drum, the thun-der-ing drum, the thun-der-ing drum. The
thun-der-ing drum, the thun-der-ing drum, the thun-der-ing drum. The

charge, charge, charge,

charge, charge, charge,

charge, charge, charge,

charge, charge, charge,

charge, charge,

charge, charge,

charge, charge,

charge, charge,

Sing any notes and randomly gliss. up and down until J , then hold.
Breathe individually when necessary. Convey horror!

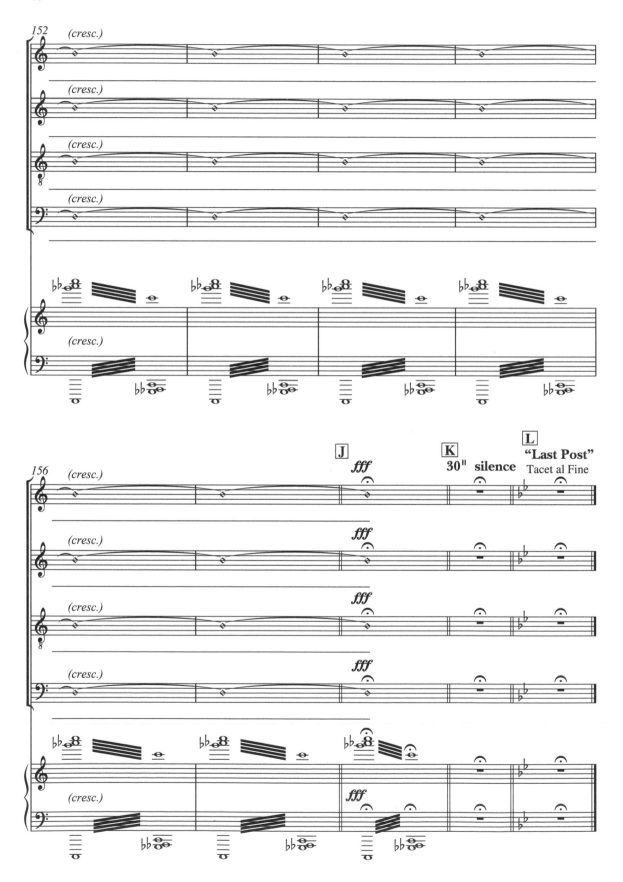

8. Angry Flames

Text: Toge Sankichi

Note. In the composer's own performances of this work this movement commences with four bars of bell strokes. The violins' entry occurs in the fifth bar (numbered bar 1 in order to agree with pre-existing scores), and trumpet 1 enters in the seventh bar (bar 3).

* All solos in this movement may be sung by a mezzo-soprano, with octave transposition as appropriate

9. Torches

Text: The Mahàbhàrata *

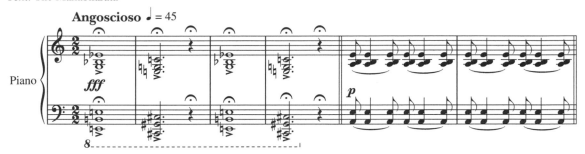

* *The Mahàbhàrata (Adi Parva, The Khandava – daha Parva), begun 6th century BC.*

Translation © copyright 2000 by The Trustees of the Armouries

78

10. Agnus Dei

11. Now the Guns have Stopped

Text: Guy Wilson

- lone; And must try to live life as be - fore And hide my grief.

For you, my dear - est friend, who should be with me now,

Not cold, too_____ soon,___ And in your grave, A - lone.

12. Benedictus

* If no cello soloist available, start at bar 27.

88

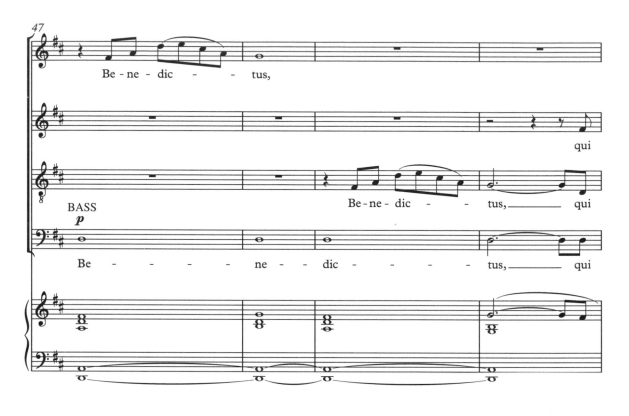

90

13. Better is Peace

Text: Mallory/anon/Tennyson/Revelation 21:4

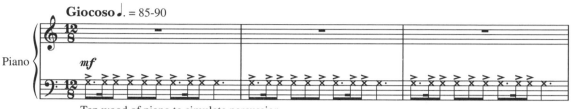

Tap wood of piano to simulate percussion.

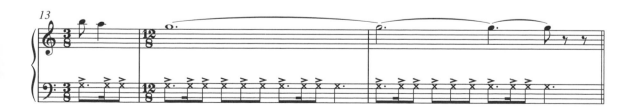

A
"Lancelot"– Solo
(Optional TENOR or BASS)
16
mf
Bet - ter is peace than al - ways war, al - ways war, bet - ter is peace than
"Lancelot"– Solo
(Optional TENOR or BASS)
mf
Bet - ter is peace than al - ways war, al - ways war, bet - ter is peace than
"Guinevere"– Solo
18
(Optional SOPRANO or ALTO)
mf
And bet - ter is peace than ev - er- more war,
"Guinevere"– Solo
(Optional SOPRANO or ALTO)
mf
And bet - ter is peace than ev - er- more war,
al - ways war, al - ways war,
al - ways war, al - ways war,
20
bet - ter is peace than ev - er - more war, and bet - ter and bet - ter is peace,
bet - ter is peace than ev - er - more war, and bet - ter and bet - ter is peace,

SOPRANO solo

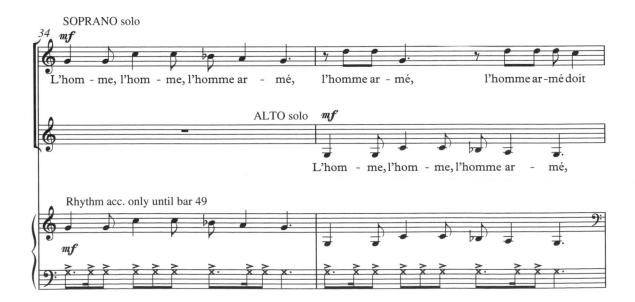

L'hom - me, l'hom - me, l'homme ar - mé, l'homme ar - mé, l'homme ar - mé doit

ALTO solo *mf*

L'hom - me, l'hom - me, l'homme ar - mé,

Rhythm acc. only until bar 49

104

110

112

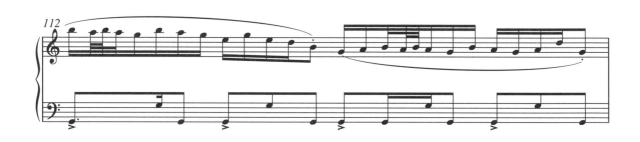

114

118

122